GARFIELD
TALK TO THE
PAW

JIM DAVIS

GW00375117

ℛℛ
RAVETTE PUBLISHING

First published by Ravette Publishing 2009.

Printed in the UK by CPI Bookmarque, Croydon, CR0 4TD
for Ravette Publishing Limited,
PO Box 876
Horsham
West Sussex RH12 9GH

ISBN: 978-1-84161-317-8

DOGS PUT WAY TOO MUCH EFFORT INTO DOING NOTHING

JIM DAVIS 1-13

www.garfield.com

Distributed by Universal Press Syndicate

SLAP

TAG TEAM BEGGING

JIM DAVIS 1-27

WHIRRRRR..

JIM DAVIS 2-28

IS THAT A CHAIN?

I'VE PUT ON A LITTLE WEIGHT, OKAY?!

JIM DAVIS 3-3

JIM DAVIS 4-22

CUPCAKES

MADE YOU SMILE

JIM DAVIS 4-23

OTHER GARFIELD BOOKS AVAILABLE

Pocket Books	**Price**	**ISBN**
Am I Bothered?	£3.99	978-1-84161-286-7
Compute This!	£3.50	978-1-84161-194-5
Don't Ask!	£3.99	978-1-84161-247-8
Feed Me!	£3.99	978-1-84161-242-3
Get Serious	£3.99	978-1-84161-265-2
Gooooal!	£3.99	978-1-84161-329-1
Gotcha!	£3.50	978-1-84161-226-3
I Am What I Am!	£3.99	978-1-84161-243-0
I Don't Do Perky	£3.99	978-1-84161-195-2
Kowabunga	£3.99	978-1-84161-246-1
Numero Uno	£3.99	978-1-85304-297-3
Pop Star	£3.50	978-1-84161-151-8
S.W.A.L.K.	£3.50	978-1-84161-225-6
Time to Delegate	£3.99	978-1-84161-296-6
Wan2tlk?	£3.99	978-1-84161-264-5
What's Not to Like?	£3.99	978-1-84161-285-0
Theme Books		
Creatures Great & Small	£3.99	978-1-85304-998-9
Entertains You	£4.50	978-1-84161-221-8
Pigging Out	£4.50	978-1-85304-893-7
Slam Dunk!	£4.50	978-1-84161-222-5
The Seasons	£3.99	978-1-85304-999-6
2-in-1 Theme Books		
All In Good Taste	£6.99	978-1-84161-209-6
Easy Does It	£6.99	978-1-84161-191-4
Lazy Daze	£6.99	978-1-84161-208-9
Licensed to Thrill	£6.99	978-1-84161-192-1
Out For The Couch	£6.99	978-1-84161-144-0
The Gruesome Twosome	£6.99	978-1-84161-143-3
Classics		
Volume One	£6.99	978-1-85304-970-5
Volume Two	£7.99	978-1-85304-971-2
Volume Three	£7.99	978-1-85304-996-5
Volume Four	£6.99	978-1-85304-997-2
Volume Five	£6.99	978-1-84161-022-1
Volume Six	£6.99	978-1-84161-023-8
Volume Seven	£5.99	978-1-84161-088-7
Volume Eight	£6.99	978-1-84161-089-4
Volume Nine	£6.99	978-1-84161-149-5
Volume Ten	£6.99	978-1-84161-150-1
Volume Eleven	£7.99	978-1-84161-175-4
Volume Twelve	£6.99	978-1-84161-176-1
Volume Thirteen	£6.99	978-1-84161-206-5
Volume Fourteen	£6.99	978-1-84161-207-2
Volume Fifteen	£5.99	978-1-84161-232-4
Volume Sixteen	£5.99	978-1-84161-233-1

Classics (cont'd ...)	Price	ISBN
Volume Seventeen	£7.99	978-1-84161-250-8
Volume Eighteen	£6.99	978-1-84161 251-5
Volume Nineteen	£6.99	978-1-84161-303-1
Volume Twenty	£6.99	978-1-84161 304-8

Gift Books

	Price	ISBN
30 years - the fun's just begun	£9.99	978-1-84161-307-9
Don't Know, Don't Care	£4.99	978-1-84161-279-9
Get a Grip	£4.99	978-1-84161-282-9
I Don't Do Ordinary	£4.99	978-1-84161-281-2
Keep your Attitude, I have my own	£4.99	978-1-84161-278-2

Little Books

	Price	ISBN
C-c-c-caffeine	£2.50	978-1-84161-183-9
Food 'n' Fitness	£2.50	978-1-84161-145-7
Laughs	£2.50	978-1-84161-146-4
Love 'n' Stuff	£2.50	978-1-84161-147-1
Surf 'n' Sun	£2.50	978-1-84161-186-0
The Office	£2.50	978-1-84161-184-6
Zzzzzz	£2.50	978-1-84161-185-3

Miscellaneous

	Price	ISBN
Colour Collection Book 3 (Aug 09)	£11.99	978-1-84161-320-8
Colour Collection Book 2	£10.99	978-1-84161-306-2
Colour Collection Book 1	£10.99	978-1-84161-293-5
Treasury 7	£10.99	978-1-84161-248-5
Treasury 6	£10.99	978-1-84161-229-4
Treasury 5	£10.99	978-1-84161-198-3
Treasury 4	£10.99	978-1-84161-180-8
Treasury 3	£9.99	978-1-84161-142-6

All Garfield books are available at your local bookshop or from the publisher at the address below.

Just send your order with your payment and name and address details to:-

Ravette Publishing Ltd
PO Box 876
Horsham
West Sussex RH12 9GH
(tel: 01403 711443 ... email: ingrid@ravettepub.co.uk)

Prices and availability are subject to change without notice.

Please enclose a cheque or postal order made payable to **Ravette Publishing** to the value of the cover price of the book/s and allow the following for UK postage and packing:-

70p for the first book + 40p for each additional book
except Treasuries & Colour Collections... when please add £3.00 per book